Believe
In
Make-Believe

*A true story of a child learning the
ultimate truth about make-believe*

From the Tooth Fairy, to Santa Claus, to the Easter Bunny,
experience the inner thoughts of a child as the innocence
of her beliefs is invaded by a reality that threatens her
search for truth.

By
Stephen F

ISBN 0-9774749-3-3

Table of Contents

Dedication   - iv-
Author's Bio   - vi-
Publisher's Prologue   - viii-

Chapter One   - 1-
Chapter Two   - 9-
Chapter Three   - 24-
Chapter Four   - 33-
Chapter Five   - 37-
Chapter Six   - 40-
Chapter Seven   - 43-
Chapter Eight   - 45-
Chapter Nine   - 48-

Dedication

I want to first dedicate this book to the Lord for believing in me and for blessing me with this incredible experience I now share with you. I also dedicate this book to my beautiful daughters, Avery and Meagan, who have blessed my life beyond words. The love and life we share has truly given me an ultimate joy and purpose for living. I love you.

Author's Bio

Stephen Fanning has been an independent television producer and professional photographer for over twenty five years. Through his unique creative talents, he specializes in creating, writing, and producing television commercials and promotional video presentations for non-profit organizations, churches, and numerous businesses and corporations. Over the years, his photographic career has allowed him to build an extensive gallery of photographs from around the world.

Now, as an author, Stephen continues to work in television and photographic production as he expands his writing career. His previous book, *Who is Clay?* was written in 2006. He lives with his two daughters, Avery and Meagan Fanning, in San Antonio, Texas. Learn more about the author at <u>www.stevefanning.com</u>.

Prologue by Publisher

As a publisher of children's books, we were delighted when Stephen Fanning decided to become part of the Entry Way team. Not only were we excited about his book, *Who is CLAY*, which he's allowing us to republish, but we were thrilled to become his first-time publisher of this precious story about the reality of magic, make-believe, and truth.

Believe in Make-Believe is very special to me and I am very proud to be able to be a part of offering a spiritual message of God's love to those that might receive it.

One of the reasons that this book is so special to me is because it brings back one of my fondest memories of how I found God. As a three-year-old child, I had watched other children on Sunday mornings go past our window. The girls and boys all looked more dressed up than usual and they looked happier than usual. I too wanted to be a part of this special trip. However, my mother sadly explained to me that we did not have enough money for me to have just the right dress or just the right shoes in order to go where the children were going… *Sunday school*, mom called it.

Stephen Fanning

Well, I only watched my friends go a couple of more times before I slipped out the front door and dressed in my usual messy casuals, I followed right along with the children to a church, only blocks away from our garage apartment.

The Sunday school teacher scooped me up in her loving arms and asked me my name. I'll never forget her face or the feeling I received when she cared enough to inquire about me. Holding me in her lap, the teacher then told me about Jesus. We sang a song that day, which had the words in it, 'All the children of the world', and I'll never forget those words or how they made me feel loved in a way I had never before experienced.

Of course, that day my mother was very angry with me when I turned up missing. She went to a great deal of trouble to find me. However, when the Sunday school teacher brought me home all dressed up in a pretty pink Sunday dress and a pair of *loaner*, patent leather shoes, she smiled and forgave me.

Stephen Fanning's book brings to the world this same special feeling I was given as a baby in God's world. The feeling is called 'unconditional love'; and he describes it well by sharing that there is a big difference between *make-believe* and *truth*. At the same time, Stephen teaches us that both are equally important. He shows us that just knowing that the world will pick us individually out of a universe of other children just to show us that we are important, is one of the traditions that should never be lost.

Entry Way Publishing is honored to help Stephen keep the traditions of the Tooth Fairy, Santa, and the Easter Bunny alive and well – so that these feelings will live on for an eternity. Keeping these much-needed belief systems alive allows millions of children all over the world to continue seeing their special qualities. *Make-believe* and *God's truth* both allow all of us to know that we are loved – no matter what.

Enjoy Avery, her sister Meagan and don't forget to put your tooth under your pillow, you'll never know what it might bring.

Thank you Stephen for bringing my youthful memories to surface once again and for the opportunity to get to know you and your extra-special daughters.

VicToria Freudiger, Founder – Entry Way Publishing.

Chapter One
Grandmother's House

Grandmother's house lived up to expectation. The four of us were winding down from an event-laden, candy-filled day that one would experience while visiting your typical *grandmother's house*. This house belonged to Anne, the grandmother to my wife, Debbie. I guess you could call it *great-grandmother's house* as well, since Anne was the great-grandmother to our beautiful daughters, Avery and Meagan.

It was late, close to midnight. The battle to go to bed had begun several hours earlier. "Girls, you need to go to sleep!" Debbie and I had pleaded with them numerous times. We had already gone through the usual reasons why our daughters felt they needed to get out of bed. Each had gone to the bathroom twice, drank their cup of water to quench their dying thirst, prayed, adjusted the nightlight, heard a bedtime story, and even had their backs scratched. On a normal night at home, these excuses come into play, but at *grandmother's house*, the chore of going to bed is usually much more difficult.

After all, that is the way it always should be when you stay at your grandparents' house. The rules not only change, they don't seem to exist. In fact, rules usually get left at Mom and Dad's house. They don't get included in the overnight suitcase filled with teddy bears, videos, games, and cookies. At your grandparents' house, you're the king or queen, you set the rules, you get the delicious pleasure of being able to have Oreos and milk for your main course at dinner, and last but not least, you go to bed only when your body does it for you.

A grandparents' house is truly like heaven. It is there you learn what unconditional love is really all about. They are not only your *master*, but they live for you, and are happy only if you are happy. It doesn't matter where you've come from, what you have done, or what mood you're in; once you are there, you no longer have to worry.

To me, God is a grandparent. He answers to whatever childish name we give Him. God doesn't mind *what* we call Him just as long as we *do* call Him. Sure, I know there are rules and my grandparents and parents knew there were rules, but those rules came in a distant second to the love and devotion I received from them. I never knew they could be angry with me. That word wasn't in their vocabulary. My joy was my grandparents' goal. They worked so hard to make me happy. My happiness was the only thing I felt made them happy. As I grew up, I followed the rules not to avoid their potential anger; I followed the rules because I did not want to disappoint them. I learned the rules were there not to show some sort of allegiance to them. The rules were there to make my life better - to make me happy. For then and only then, would my grandparents be happy.

I can't image God being any less loving and understanding than my grandparents. And to think He can be more loving is beyond my comprehension. What I did understand was, at this moment, I was trying to instill just one rule to my girls here at grandmother's house. Go to bed.

"Mommy, Daddy, we're scared sleeping in that room all alone," the girls whined while walking into our normally assigned room. Usually, they slept together in their room, but by not being in the comfort of their own home, the girls were uneasy about the new living environment at grandmother's house. Giving the saddest look each child could muster, the girls stood slumped over one another while clutching their own cherished blanket.

My wife, Debbie, and I thought our daughters were down to their last excuse for avoiding bedtime. As parents, it was time to tag team. Debbie went with five-year-old Meagan to sleep back in the *scary* room, while eight-year-old Avery climbed into bed with me. Finally, the lights were out. It was now quiet at grandmother's house and I drifted toward sleep.

"Dad, it came out!" Avery exclaimed as she held up her prized trophy. I turned on the bedside lamp to shed some light on whatever was happening. The battle of going to bed had taken a turn against the parents and for the girls. The lost-tooth excuse finally won out. It wasn't Avery's first lost tooth; in fact, this one was bigger than those first few. The tooth was one of those side teeth, a molar they call it, I guess. Avery didn't care what the tooth was called, she was just glad to call it out. "It's out! It finally came out!" she yelled through her bloody smile.

At eight years of age, and five or six baby teeth later, blood from losing a tooth no longer scared her. She now realized blood came with the territory. As a parent, I have yet to get accustomed to the sight of blood on one of my children. Who does? The image of my daughter's happy face highlighted by the stark contrast of her beautiful smile filled with blood is just another one of life's unusual photographs.

"It's a big one!" I said, cleaning the tooth off with my thumb. I was happy for her, but felt a tinge of sadness while staring at the small reminder that my little girl was growing up. Piece by piece, tooth by tooth, bits and pieces of her childhood kept falling away, every day, to reveal a beautiful grown up young lady.

Avery interrupted my thoughts by grabbing the tooth. She ran off to the *scary* bedroom to show it to her mommy and to younger sister, Meagan. At five years of age, Meagan had yet to lose a tooth. I knew she would be happy for Avery, but at the same time, she may be a little jealous. I would be too. After all, the score was Avery, six teeth lost; Meagan, zero. We were only minutes away from the *tooth-pulling* subject being brought up again by Meagan. I could see it coming.

Debbie said what every mother instinctively knows to say; "Avery, let's go rinse your mouth with warm salt water." Off to the kitchen they went as Meagan came into my room to persuade me to pull her *loose* teeth.

"I don't care if it does hurt, Daddy. This tooth right here is ready to come out!" Meagan petitioned.

"It sure feels loose to me," I said, while making it look as though I was attempting to pull one of her baby teeth. Failing once again, I said, "It's almost ready but let's give it a few more days."

As a father, I didn't mind if Meagan was much older before she lost one of her precious baby teeth. Even though she was frowning, I made certain to make another mental snapshot of her beautiful smile filled with all of her baby teeth. Days blessed with that smile, I knew, were fleeting and I was happy to fail again at pulling one of her teeth.

Anyway, so much for a good night's sleep. It might as well have been twelve-noon rather than past midnight by all the activity. In came Mommy with Avery who was all cleaned up. The blood was gone, but the smile with a new hole on the side remained. All four of us sat on grandmother's vintage four-poster guest bed. *Please don't break,* I thought. *We'll never get any sleep!*

"Daddy, does the Tooth Fairy come even if we're not at our own house?" Avery asked.

"Of course she does," encouraged Debbie. "The Tooth Fairy knows where you are all the time."

"But how does she know I'm here at grandma's house? Who told her?" asked Avery. Like her teeth, the baby questions were beginning to be replaced with more mature ones.

Debbie gave me that look that told me it was my turn to answer. "Well, Avery, she just does, and, uh, aren't you glad she can find you here?" I stammered.

Instead of answering, our daughter simply sat there lost in her own thoughts looking at her tooth. I felt my answer no longer quite cut it. You could detect the touch of a new ingredient being introduced into her young childlike mind. Call it reason, logic, or reality; this new ingredient was competing with Avery's previous beliefs. She seemed to let me off the hook and placed her thoughts on the shelf - for now.

"Let's go to bed now so the Tooth Fairy can come!" Debbie suggested.

"Yeah, that's a great idea." I seconded my wife's idea while nestling under the covers. Avery got in the bed and carefully placed the prized tooth under her pillow next to me. Before leaving to go to her room with Meagan, Debbie mouthed the words to me, "Good luck!" She closed the door leaving both of us in the darkness of the guest bedroom at grandmother's house.

I waited. And I waited some more, listening for any evidence that Avery was asleep. I knew the Tooth Fairy needed to come soon, but the Tooth Fairy was about to fall asleep himself. Though struggling to stay awake, I was encouraged when Avery finally quit tossing and turning. All that was left was for me to hear the sound of regular, constant breathing. We've all been there, waiting for someone to pass into dreamland. I had it all planned out and had taken the only money I had out of my wallet and had placed it under *my* pillow, a five-dollar bill. That's it. That's all I had. I smiled in the dark thinking how much the Tooth Fairy fee had gone up since I was a child. More time slipped by. Was she asleep? She had to be! Her breathing settled and it was time for me to make the switch.

Chapter Two
Meet the Tooth Fairy

Slowly I slid my hand underneath her pillow and took hold of the tooth. I pulled it out and waited. Her breathing was the same. So far, so good. I waited some more. I folded up the five-dollar bill and slid the money as far as possible under Avery's pillow. Leaving it there, I brought my hand out. It was done. I was so proud of the fact that I –

"Daddy, was that you?" Like an alarm blaring to the thief in the night, Avery had caught me. Silence. "Daddy, did you do what I think you just did?" Avery whispered. My thoughts raced. *What do I say?* She sat up immediately, turned on the lamp and lifted her pillow. The tooth was gone and a folded-up five-dollar bill was all that was left. "Daddy, did you do this?"

There are times in life when I would do anything to keep from dealing with the truth. This was one of them. This was a moment of truth and I could see it coming. "Well yes, Avery, I put the money there."

She thought for a moment. "Why did you do that? What about the Tooth Fairy? Isn't the Tooth Fairy supposed to do this?"

I knew my daughter needed to be told the truth; yet, I longed for her to be able to remain a child; to enjoy childhood dreams and hopes; to believe in make-believe, in fairytales and in the happily-ever-after. I began, "No, honey, uh..., since we're on vacation at grandma's house, I decided to act as the Tooth Fairy and help her do her job." Now that was a pretty lame excuse, I know, but I was trying to get as close to the truth as possible without being too obvious and without lying to her. After all, my answer was sort of true. I was helping out the other *Tooth Fairy* who was sleeping soundly with Meagan in the *scary* room.

Avery analyzed me. With her mental wheels turning, she gave me a concerned stare. "Dad, what does that mean? Are you helping out the Tooth Fairy or are *you* the Tooth Fairy?"

"Well, the time had come for the whole truth. "Yes, Avery, I am," I admitted.

"Have you done this before with my other teeth?" she asked with uncertainty.

Avery had always known the right questions to ask. In this case, this was a question I didn't want to hear. "Uh, yes, Avery, I have," I admitted. My mind searched for words of explanation and comfort but it was empty at the moment.

"Why? What about the Tooth Fairy? Is there no such thing as the Tooth Fairy?" she asked intently.

"Avery, there is a Tooth Fairy but she's not like you think. In fact, you're looking at her. I'm the Tooth Fairy."

"You mean all those times I put my tooth under my pillow, it was you that replaced my tooth with the money?"

"Yes. Well, it was either me or Mommy, but one of us was always the Tooth Fairy."

Avery laid back and gazed up at the ceiling. The room was beginning to feel very quiet. Looking over to me, she said, "You mean, if there really is no Tooth Fairy, why did you and Mommy make me think there was one?"

The moment she asked me this question, I wished I had all night to think of an answer, but she needed and deserved one at that very moment. "Avery, one of the joys of being a child is make-believe. There is nothing that is more fun than being able to pretend and to use one's imagination. There is plenty of time later on in life to deal with, what grown-ups call *reality*. In fact, the older you get, the harder it will be to pretend and to believe in make-believe. As a child, I loved the excitement I felt when my mommy and daddy allowed me to believe in make-believe. To imagine the Tooth Fairy actually flying into my room, taking my tooth, and giving me a quarter was something I will never forget. The quarter was neat, but to actually think the Tooth Fairy knew that I was somebody, that she even paid attention to something as small as one of my teeth, was a feeling that made being a child so much fun. It brought some magic and excitement into my life even if it was make-believe."

"But weren't you sad when you found out there was no Tooth Fairy?" Avery asked with a tear in her eye.

"Sure, I learned one day that my mom and dad were the Tooth Fairy and that make-believe was gone; but that sadness got replaced with something even more unbelievable. My parents loved me so much that they would even act like a Tooth Fairy to make me happy. And I couldn't wait until I had children and could make their make-believe magical and exciting."

"It's still sad though," Avery said. "I mean, I've heard some of my friends say they didn't believe in the Tooth Fairy, but I always thought it was true."

"Avery, it is true. It's just a different way of believing in the Tooth Fairy. You're *looking* at the Tooth Fairy. I know I'm not as pretty as you thought the Tooth Fairy would be, but this Tooth Fairy loves you more than all the other tooth fairies in the world put together. Mommy and I will do anything to make your life happy, exciting, and something that you will remember for the rest of your life. Using your imagination or make-believe makes life exciting, especially as a child. Make-believe can be more fun than reality but after you become a grown-up, you'll find that a lot of the things you call *real* will turn out to be make-believe anyway."

"That sounds weird, Daddy!" Avery said with a small but detectable smile.

That small smile looms bigger in my memory today than the bloody, toothless one. My daughter's smile told me she was making a start at not feeling so sad. It is easy as a parent to attempt to trivialize a child's feelings. It may be a defense mechanism we use so our hearts aren't broken all over again. I had to remember that Avery was filled with very real emotions of sadness. It didn't matter what provoked her feelings. It didn't matter how petty the source of these feelings was. That was secondary. She was sad. And it was real. It reminded me of one of my favorite quotes by my father, commenting on the sincerity and absolute realness of other people's feelings. He said, "Puppy love is real to the puppy."

In the dimly lit bedroom at grandmother's house, I continued, "Avery, once you become a grownup, you'll be tempted to do what I and so many other grownups do every day. There are things out there we think are real but are actually make-believe."

"Like what?" Avery asked.

"Well, let me think. *Fear* is one," I answered. "I'll find out that something I was afraid of doesn't exist, any more than the Tooth Fairy exists. *Worry*, is another kind of bad Tooth Fairy. I'll worry about things that, when I try to touch them, are not there. Do you remember when you used to believe there was a monster under your bed?"

Avery answered by turning her smile into a small, short giggle.

Her giggle encouraged me to continue; "You don't believe that any more, do you? Neither do I, but that fear kept you awake at night, didn't it? It did me. The older you get, the more you outgrow those fears. In fact, you can even laugh about them one day. However, it's easy to *replace* them with more grownup, make-believe fears. What used to be monsters under our bed turn into monsters in our head. I know that may sound weird but one day, you'll understand. I'll stay up at night worrying about things that are no more real than the Tooth Fairy or the monster under my bed. And one day I'll probably laugh about them too."

Avery was now staring down at her five-dollar bill, yet I could tell she was actually focusing intently on her thoughts. What was she thinking? What questions filled her mind? I decided to keep trying to answer; "Our whole life we make ourselves believe certain things in a certain way, whether it is good make-believe or bad make-believe. Now that you've learned there is no Tooth Fairy, you'll make up what you will believe about the Tooth Fairy from now on. You can be sad that the Tooth Fairy, you once believed in, does not exist, or you can be happy that you and Meagan live with the Tooth Fairy every day. Mommy and I don't have wings, but you now know just how far we will go to fill your life with love, joy, and an excitement about every little thing that happens in your life. Avery, the one thing in all of this that is true and will always be true is that we love you more than you will ever know. That's what is real in all of this."

She kept analyzing the money in her hand and the thoughts in her head for what seemed a lifetime. I was more worn out than the five-dollar bill. What else could I say? I don't even know where most of the things I said came from anyway. I've never heard God's actual voice, but I've heard what God means for me to hear many times. I believe His voice is heard through the mouths and words of others. Whether it is the collection of words on a page or in a song, or the loving voice of my family, my friends, my church, or my inner, *still small voice* that exists permanently in my own thoughts, God can be heard. In fact, I believe God speaks through anyone's voice if they use words to try to help others, even if that voice happens to be your own. His voice is there. It's just a matter of if I want to listen to it.

"Okay, Daddy," she finally said. "Thanks for telling me."

"Do you want to ask me anything or tell me anything else?" I asked.

"No. I think I'm okay right now," she answered.

"Do you want to try to get to sleep now? We can always talk more about it in the morning," I suggested through a half-hearted yawn.

"Yeah, I guess so."

"Avery, if you don't mind, why don't we let Meagan still believe in the Tooth Fairy, since she hasn't even started losing her teeth yet. Okay?" I asked, wondering where this might lead.

"Oh, sure, Daddy. I know my sister still needs to make-believe in the Tooth Fairy. I won't tell her."

"Well, thank you, Avery. You're the best big sister Meagan could ever have. I know the Tooth Fairy will be even more special for her now that you can help Mommy and me be the Tooth Fairy," I suggested with a sleepy but genuine smile.

"Night-night," she said while turning off her lamp.

"Night-night, Avery. I love you," I whispered, in the dark at grandmother's house.

I don't know how much time passed. It hadn't taken me long to doze off. You know the routine. You lie in bed and find that comfortable position where everything is just right. The cool side of the pillow fits; the covers are tucked in where they need to be. With eyes closed, you wait for your thoughts to drift. They drift a little; and then more, and more. I was at that point, on the verge of plunging off the edge into that welcomed relief called sleep. Who knows, I may have already been there…

"Daddy," she said. "Daddy," she said again, a tiny bit louder. I think she said it twice. But however many times she said it, she used that tone of voice that doesn't want to wake you up but needs to get your attention as politely as possible.

"Yes Avery," I said, I think.

"Can I ask you just one more question?" she whispered. By the sound of her voice, she hadn't even thought about sleep. She was awake as awake could be. Whatever this question was, I knew it had done a good job of keeping her wide awake. I've had those too, questions that take over your thoughts; that hold you hostage, never relenting, never ceasing. Generally, it's just one question, but that one question is usually plenty. No matter how often your body pleads with you for sleep, that one question can take over like a virus. Sure, I remember a few of those questions but most of those questions have faded to nothingness in my memory.

Isn't that funny? Some major question is so important that we will worship it with our worry no matter what time of day it is. In fact, the question generally lies dormant during the day and becomes infectious to our every thought between one o'clock and about six o'clock in the morning. Yet, as time goes by, we may remember back to staying up all night worrying about some question, but we somehow forget what most of those questions had been.

Generally, during one of those questions, or a time of stress or anger, I try to ask myself, "Will I remember this tomorrow? Will I remember this next week? Next month will I remember this? Will I remember this next year? Will I remember this for the rest of my life?"

The longer it takes me to answer *no,* should help me determine the importance of the situation. This seems to help me when I will allow it to work. There are times though, when I'm just in the mood to worry. I don't care how unimportant the situation is, I want to worry, get mad, or get stressed. Maybe it's because I feel I don't have anything else to do at the moment.

Sure, I've had a few life-changing experiences where I answered, "Yes, I will remember this for the rest of my life." Yet, for each one of those events, I have had thousands of so-called important concerns or questions that didn't even remain in my memory the following day. However, at the time, that question seemed to mean everything to me. It was all knowing and all consuming; a question happening in the *here and now*.

And *now*, is where we were, in the dark, in the middle of the night, in grandmother's house. On this night, Avery had one of those questions.

"What is it, Avery?" I whispered while trying to clear my thoughts.

"Daddy, J.D. (the boy next door) and I were talking the other day and he told me that his parents admitted to him they were the Tooth Fairy and that they were the Easter Bunny and Santa Claus, too." Avery paused, seeming to brace herself for the ultimate question as she continued, "Uh, Daddy? Does that mean there really is no Easter Bunny and no Santa Claus?"

I should have known this question was coming. After all, for the past year or so we had flirted with this issue several times, especially about Santa Claus. It might have been in the car, driving home from a birthday party, or sometime during dinner when Avery would ask an indirect question about Santa. Most of the time a question on this subject had ended with a usual cloned answer such as, "Sure, there is a Santa Claus!" Avery never came out to challenge the issue, but I knew her maturing mind had been battling with the logic versus the magic of Santa Claus and the Easter Bunny for some time. Maybe she didn't want to confront the potential truth about them. Until now.

But couldn't it have been on a different night? Or even during the day? It always helps to learn stark reality while the sun is shining. But surely, not on the same night the image of her Tooth Fairy had been destroyed. I asked God for wisdom in my words. If I ever needed them, it was now. In the pitch darkness of grandmother's house, there was nothing else to do but confront Santa Claus and the Easter Bunny head on.

"Avery, just like the Tooth Fairy, there comes a time when you learn to believe in things in a different way. There is no Santa Claus and Easter Bunny like you have believed growing up. Still, it doesn't mean they are not real, it just means they don't exist the way you thought they did. The magical beliefs as a child wear off the older we get, but the feelings that come out of those beliefs remain forever. That is where the truth remains.

What makes Santa Claus and the Easter Bunny fun is not whether or not they exist. What truly matters are the feelings of love and joy you receive. You don't even remember all the presents that Santa brings. Most of them get thrown out with the next garage sale. What you remember is that you are somebody. You are important. You are loved so much that someone would come from the northern most part of the world and land on your roof, just to give you presents and to eat your cookies. I remember thinking, 'You mean, the Easter Bunny will take time out of his busy schedule just to visit me?' That made me feel good inside. I was special. Children like to believe these stories because it makes them feel special, important, and, most importantly, loved. And, you know what, Avery; you're still loved more than you will ever know. The only thing that has changed is how you know you are loved."

There was silence, except for the small yet detectable sound of Avery's labored breathing. She was crying. My little girl was crying hard and she was hurt. I know her hurt was sincere because she was doing everything she could to conceal it from me. My chest was heavy and my heart was physically hurting. It was breaking with the pain my little girl was going through. I would have taken it all from her if I could.

Chapter Three
Searching for the Answers

Gazing up at the ceiling consumed in darkness, I began looking for more words to say. I hate nights like this, where the only light in the tunnel of your sleepless thoughts comes momentarily through the window from the passing car's headlights. Like your hope, the light shows up, dances across the room for mere seconds, and fades back into the darkness, leaving you alone. The weight of the darkness was heavy and the silence of the room was stifling. There was no hope at the moment, no passing car, nothing. Finally, Avery broke the silence. "So if there is no Santa Claus or Easter Bunny, why does everybody talk about them and pretend they are real?"

Good question, again. At least she asked something because asking nothing seemed worse. We were moving. I didn't know if we were moving forward or backward, but at least my daughter and I weren't stuck in the mud of our own thoughts.

It was my turn to talk now. "I guess because it's a way for parents to help make being a child so much fun. The truth in all of this is that you and Meagan are loved beyond words. And as parents, we will do anything and everything, even by creating some make-believe, to show you the ultimate truth of our love. As you grow up, your feelings will change. Your way of seeing things will change, but after you've become a grown-up, I hope and pray you will see that it was love that led us. Our love for you is the most real thing in the world and is unchanging. It is love that makes us do any and everything we can for you to make your life special and full of joy."

In the darkness, I could feel Avery's presence next to me. I could sense her awareness and knew she was listening intently, so I continued. "I remember when you and Meagan were babies, and Mommy or I would hold each of you as you rode the mechanical horsy outside of the Wal-Mart. We would scream and laugh and say, 'Isn't this fun?' You would hang on for dear life, laughing and enjoying the feelings you were having. You were happy, excited, and maybe, a little scared, but you both loved it. And as parents, we even played a little make-believe acting like the ride also scared us. Well now, that same ride doesn't have the magic it once did. But it's still there. Maybe you no longer remember the excitement of the ride, but I hope you remember that we spent that quarter and rode that ride with you to make you happy and, above all, to show you in any way and every way that we loved you. Chances are little that you will want to ride that horsy again until you hold your own child as he or she rides it one day. You'll laugh and scream, using a little make-believe, to make your child feel excited. Why will you do this? Because you will want him or her to have the best life possible, filled with excitement, joy, and, above all, your love. That is where the truth is."

More silence stifled the darkness while an occasional sound of a sniffle reminded me that Avery was still crying. I was tempted to keep talking as if my words would fill up the emptiness that permeated the still dark air. What else could I say? I felt I had talked too much already. Outside, a car drove by. The brief hum of its engine and the sound of the tires meeting the road brought a welcomed respite to the heavy silence that filled the room. As the light from the headlights danced across the darkened walls, I yearned for it to stay for a while, to brighten our thoughts and to fill my little girl with some hope that she desperately needed. The light fled. It was dark again and it was quiet at grandmother's house.

"Okay, Daddy. I know what you're saying, but how do you know what to believe anymore? I mean, how do you know what is really true?"

"Well, Avery," I began, not knowing where I would end up, "I'm still trying to figure that one out myself too. Some things are true because you just know they are true. There are other things that are not true, but they should be; or maybe they are true, just in a different way."

"Uh-huh," she responded. I took that to mean, "Okay, Dad, I sort of understand so far."

At least she was listening. I just prayed I was giving her words worth listening to. "What

27

I'm trying to say is that some things on the surface may not be actually true but the main meaning behind the story is true. It's not whether a story is true but whether the story contains truth."

"But, Daddy, a lot of times people will say something is true even though you can't see it. So it's hard to know what to believe sometimes."

"Everybody has that question. Sometimes more than others, but you'll find out that truth has a way of really convincing you what the truth is. The most important things in the world are invisible when you think about it. Gravity, wind, heat are some of those things in science you'll learn about that we can't see, but there are even more important things we live with every day that we can't see. Can you think of one?"

Avery thought for a moment before answering, "I don't know. I guess - *feelingscared*? Or dreaming? Or things like that?"

"That's right! And the most important invisible thing I live with every day is *love*. I love you with my whole life, and guess what; I cannot see it or touch it, but I know my love for you is as true as anything in the world. Just like the love Jesus has for us, my love is similar. I have never seen Him, but I know the truth and that truth is that Jesus loves all of us. We can't see Him, but we feel His presence and we are able to see all of the wonderful things He does for us each day."

"Still, sometimes it's just hard to figure out," Avery said while mired in deep thought mixed in with sleepiness.

"You're right. And you'll spend your whole life still trying to understand all of this. That doesn't mean you need to be sad about it. Instead, pray to God to help you learn more about Him and the world, and above all, to enjoy every minute of your life as you grow and learn more. There's a word for that and it's called faith. In a way, faith is make-believe. What I mean is when you just know, in your heart, that some things contain the truth, you have to *make* yourself *believe* in those unseen things and in the things you hope for. Though you cannot see God, you just know He is the truth. Have faith in God and He will show you the truth. He wants you to mainly learn not necessarily what is true but *what is the truth.* Because answering the question, *What is the truth?* is more important than the question, *What is true?"*

"What do you mean by that, Daddy? Aren't they the same?"

"Most of the time they are the same. For instance, let's talk about two things. First, we have a dog whose name is Barkley, and second, you love him. Right? Both of these things are true and there is truth in both of these things. Okay?"

"Yeah, that's right. I do love Barkley," she admitted.

"And guess what, Avery, you can see Barkley, but the love you have for Barkley is invisible. You can't see it. Right? But you know with all your heart that your love for him is the truth. The fact that he is our dog is true and the fact that you love him is the truth. There are other times though where the facts may be true or not true but the message of the story has truth in it from beginning to end."

Avery perked up. "Tell me a story like that."

I thought for a moment and remembered one I had experienced. "You'll hear stories someday, true stories, where the actual facts either change or are remembered differently by the people telling the story. When your grandparents, or one of your friend's grandparents talk about how they fell in love on their first date, Grandma may say they had chocolate cake for dessert during their first dinner together. However, Granddad might tell us, 'No we didn't have chocolate cake; we had pecan pie; remember!' The story will continue with details about the events surrounding the story being either agreed upon or questioned as being true. But, the bottom-line, the ultimate fact, or the main truth about the story is what?"

"That Grandma and Granddad fell in love on their first date?" Avery answered.

"That's right. It's the truth that counts. In fact, even in the Bible, one story about Jesus says there was one angel at the empty tomb. Another story says there were two. Whether those little details are true do not really matter, do they? The main truth was, and is, that Jesus Christ was alive! He had risen from the grave and He is alive today! I didn't see it myself, but I know it's the truth just as much as I know I love you. And I can't see that love either. I just know that His love for me and the love that fills our family give ultimate joy to my life."

Changing the subject, but at the same time, not changing the subject, I said, "So whether there is an actual man in a red suit named Santa Claus, who flies reindeer onto the roof of our house to deliver presents is not the main thing. The great truth is that you are loved, by Mommy, by me, by Meagan, by your whole family, by all the Santas, tooth fairies, and Easter Bunnies we make-believe about, and, most of all, by Jesus Himself, who made love for all of us in the first place."

How much more could my daughter digest in one night? I felt as though I could hear her thoughts reflecting upon our conversation as we both fought the ever-growing cloud of fatigue that continued to fill the room. Despite the importance of the moment, this cloud was winning the battle to persuade us to follow it; to drift along with it into restful, welcomed sleep. In a slurred, almost meditative tone, Avery said, "Okay, Daddy. Thank you."

"Thank you, Avery. Get a good night's sleep and remember I love you."

Chapter Four
Precious Moments

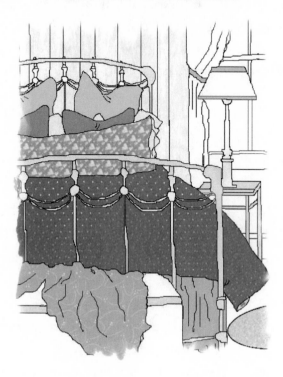

The darkness felt good now. I didn't need any more passing headlights to brighten my thoughts. What a moment! I asked the Lord to burn these last few moments into my memory forever. There are so few precious moments we have with our children that really touch the heart and soul of living. In fact, I believe these precious moments we have with our children, especially when they are very young, are memories God gives primarily to the parents, not to the children. After all, I, as a parent, remember so much more of my children's early childhood than they will. Whether it is Meagan's first steps or one of them blowing out a handful of birthday candles, our children will remember bits and pieces of these life-changing snapshots. Yet we, as parents, use every detail of these memories to continually remind us of the wonderful gift of life that God has given us. These memories are what make life worth living.

When Avery was born and I held her warm body just minutes after she came out of the womb, I remember staring into her beautiful eyes and saying, "Hello, Avery, welcome to this world. We are going to have a wonderful life together!" A moment she will never remember is a moment I will never forget. And I thank God for giving me that moment along with all the other moments our family has had together enjoying the precious gift of life our Lord and Creator has blessed us with.

Tonight was one of those precious moments; a lifetime snapshot I prayed would not fade around the edges with time. As a photographer, I capture images or video as a way to reinforce and immortalize the memory of a moment. However none of these techniques can remotely come close to preserving a memory, as touching, feeling, hugging, talking, listening, seeing, and actually being with the people and in places we love. Long ago, I decided that I wouldn't ruin my few chances to experience our family's precious moments by constantly looking at them through a video camcorder viewfinder or camera lens; thinking that, someday, it will finally bless my life. Sure, I get a few snapshots and clips of those times but I record very little of it with a mechanical device. Even what I have recorded, I don't take the time to watch because of the busyness of life.

I began asking myself, "When are all of these pictures and video going to become important enough to me to finally take time to watch and hear it all, to finally try to experience what happened? Will it be when my children are gone and I yearn for the *good old days,* when I'm old and have trouble seeing and hearing what I recorded in the first place?"

I try to use the majority of today's precious times to actually be a part of the experience. I ask God to record the memory for me, to melt it into my heart, to engrave it into my thoughts, to blend it into my soul, because those memories only get better with time.

It can be so easy to take it all for granted. My first temptation of tonight's event could have been to complain about having to stay up half the night rather than being grateful for such a wonderful experience with one of my daughters. We hadn't answered all the questions, we hadn't yet dried all the tears, but I firmly believe the truth prevailed.

God had been with us and had used this time, filled with darkness, tears, fatigue, and fears to draw us closer together and closer to Him. I knew, for sure, Avery was asleep now. And, soon after, I was there with her. Sound asleep. In the short remainder of the night, I don't think I dreamed. I didn't need to because I had just lived one.

Chapter Five
A New Day

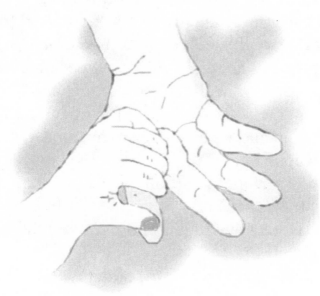

The morning light woke me from one of those good sleeps. You know the kind where you ask, "Where am I?" Coming to my senses, I remembered where I was; at *grandma's house*, as my girls would call it. The sunlight peeked directly at me through the blinds, which told me there wasn't much morning left. The sun was definitely up. It was mid-morning if not later.

I had slept well. Only then did I remember my conversation the night before with Avery. I turned to see if she was lying beside me. She was asleep facing me with her mouth partially open. I could see the space where her tooth used to be. That one tooth had created a memorable night. My precious angel was sleeping well. I lay there wondering what she was dreaming about, if anything. The door to our room opened. Debbie tiptoed in and walked over to my side of the bed. She leaned over, smiled, and whispered to me, "Good morning! We thought you were going to sleep the day away."

I looked up at her and mouthed the words, "She knows."

"What?" Debbie responded with a whisper.

"She knows. Last night she learned the truth about the Tooth Fairy." Debbie's expression changed from one highlighted with her smile to one filled with a combination of surprise, sadness, and concern. I continued, "Not only that, she learned the truth about Santa Claus and the Tooth Fairy, all in one night." I mouthed, making just enough sound for my wife to hear me.

Debbie's face looked heart-broken. "How is she? Is she okay?"

"I can't talk now but I actually think she'll be fine. I'll tell you the details later, but I can only say our talk was one I will remember the rest of my life. Just know she's fine. I think. I can only say that our talk couldn't have been better as far as I'm concerned."

"Are you sure?" Debbie asked. My wife's expression deepened with sadness as she looked over at our daughter sleeping soundly beside me. "This just breaks my heart!"

"Don't worry, Debbie. I can't put into words how special our talk was last night. I really do believe everything will be all right. In fact, I think, everything is even better. We'll talk later."

I got out of bed and ate a late breakfast. Avery was awake by now. She didn't seem happy, nor did she seem sad, but kept fairly much to herself. I dressed for the day while she ate breakfast. Later, Debbie told me Avery had gone outside by herself in the backyard.

Chapter Six
The Backyard Swing

The backyard swing at grandmother's house had been there forever. In fact, the bark from the overhanging tree branch had nearly grown over the two frayed ropes hanging down to the board Avery was sitting on. This same exact swing had filled Debbie's childhood days with fun and joy. Now her daughter, my daughter Avery, sat there. She was not swinging. My precious child was sitting there slowly dangling, her foot pushing the ground ever so slightly, moving slowly back and forth. Her blanket, the one she carried with her all the time since birth, hung on the branch above her. Avery's face was down, staring into the grass, thinking.

I started out the back door and saw my camera on the table. Grabbing it, I took one picture of her. The swing, the blanket, her foot on the ground, her head down, thinking; it was a simple photograph but I knew it would speak volumes to me in the future. I put the camera down and headed out into the backyard to see her. "Good morning, Avery." I said as I walked up to her from behind.

"Hi, Daddy," she said. Turning the swing around, Avery looked at me and smiled. It wasn't a toothless grin but it was a genuine smile that brightened my day more than the morning sun. It is amazing what light does to one's soul. The bright sun bathing us outdoors on a beautiful day was such a contrast to the dark, stifling void in which we had last spoke.

Chapter Seven
The Morning Light

When Jesus said, "I am the light of the world," it was no more evident than now what He meant when He spoke those words. The light, and His light, not only brighten the day, but fill our spirit with so many feelings we live on each and every day - joy, happiness, faith, purpose, and, maybe above all, hope.

"You get a good sleep, Daddy?" Avery asked. Though she kept staring at the ground, I knew her spirits were up. I could tell by her voice that things were better.

"Yeah, I slept great. How about you? How are you feeling about things today?"

"I'm doing okay." She thought for a moment. "Yeah, everything's okay now, Daddy."

"I sure hope so, Avery. You are a very special girl and I want you to be happy every moment of your life. I know there are some sad times, like last night, but I pray you can be happy again."

"I'll be alright, Daddy. Thank you for talking to me about everything. Thank you for telling me the truth."

The truth. Thank God there is a truth to be told. I don't know if the words I spoke to Avery brought out the truth or if God used our experience to reveal the truth to us. The truth is like sunlight. No matter how dark the day may be, filled with clouds of doubt and despair, eventually the truth will burn through the clouds revealing a day full of blue sky and light that warms our soul.

I looked to the blue sky and silently thanked the Lord for this experience. I asked Him to continue to guide and nurture Avery and Meagan through the wonderful, yet, at times, uncertain and frightening moments they will continue to experience as they grow up.

Chapter Eight
He Needs Me

Ever since they were born, our family bedtime prayer concluded with, "… and please help Avery and Meagan be the healthiest, happiest, and safest little girls in the whole wide world forever, Amen."

It took a few years, but one day, God impressed upon me that the only way my girls could even come close to being all these things was for me to do everything possible to be the best father in the world. Not just a good father, but the best. Sometimes there is more difference between *good* and *best,* than *good* and *bad.* God was saying, "There are some things I just cannot do without you."

Isn't that amazing? God actually limits himself, in some cases, to our ability to follow His calling, to do the work for Him. I was a Christian a long time before I realized that God actually needed me to help accomplish His work. Some things just would not happen if I did not follow His calling. Even if I justified my rejection of Him by saying, 'Well, someone else better qualified will do the job'; that simply was not the case; and is not the truth. Instead, the thing I learned was that if I don't do it, it may not ever get done.

God has tailor-made some challenges or potential accomplishments just for me and only me; and just for you, and only you. It honors me to think that God would give me a once in a lifetime responsibility over anything.

My life has changed for eternity because I believe in God. I know His love, joy, and grace will be with me forever in heaven.

But, something that changed me even more was when I realized that God believes in me. He is counting on me. I don't have to wait until I reach heaven to begin creating heaven here on earth. God needs my help! What more do you need to get up in the morning?

Chapter Nine
Grown Up

As the wind began to blow, I began to push Avery on the swing. "Daddy, who ate the carrots?" she asked.

"What are you talking about, Avery?"

"I mean, did you or Mommy eat the carrots we left out for the Easter Bunny?" she asked with a small laugh.

I was relieved by her humor. "Oh, yes I would try to make Mommy eat them. I enjoy eating the cookies and milk for Santa more than the carrots anyway!"

Avery laughed. I had never felt better. "Did you know, Avery, there are four stages of life? First, you believe in Santa. Second, you don't believe in Santa. Third, you become Santa. And, fourth, you start to look like Santa!"

"I'd rather eat the cookies and milk myself," she responded.

"Well, Avery, next Christmas, maybe you can help us. After all, Mommy and I need your help to make Santa special for Meagan, don't we? Make-believing in Santa can still be fun. I enjoy it more now than I did when I was little."

"Will I still get presents?" she asked.

"Avery, you'll always get presents from Mommy and me. Your whole life we will give you presents to show how much we love you. We will always be your Santa Claus, your Easter Bunny, and your Tooth Fairy."

"I know, Daddy. I think I understand everything for now."

"Just remember, the older you get, you'll learn what is true, what is not true, and what really is the *truth*. The truth is we love you and God loves you. The lines waiting to see to Santa Claus, that is, to the make-believe things, are always filled with children. You don't see just grown-ups in line to see Santa, do you?"

"No," Avery answered with a small laugh while she held on to the ropes as she sat swinging.

"That's right. Young people believe in make-believe, and that's okay. In fact, it wouldn't hurt a few grownups to do the same, to use their imagination they threw away once they got bigger. However, the older you get, the more you learn what really contains the truth. The lines to see God and to fill His church are generally filled with older people or grownups. That's because the longer you live life, you will be drawn to Him because He is the truth. Some grown-ups never figure it out. They believe that other things in life like money or power or being popular will give their life meaning and purpose. All that is make-believe too. There is no more truth in that than there is in being an actual Santa Claus. Many others finally admit that life filled with true happiness, joy, and meaning cannot be lived without God. It just doesn't work. They finally make themselves believe or use faith to believe in

God and realize that His love is the only thing in the world that is the truth. The younger you are when you figure this out and believe with the faith God has given you, the better your life will be."

It was mid-day now. Life was beyond good. We sat in the yard picking out pieces of grass. "How about the five bucks? Can I keep it too?" Avery asked jokingly.

"Of course you can," I said. "Enjoy being a child while you can, because it is a wonderful time. Think about it. When you lose a tooth as a child, you get five dollars. When you lose a tooth as an adult, you get to pay someone five hundred dollars to fix it!"

She laughed. I laughed. We stood up and started walking back into the house.

"Avery," I said. "If you don't mind, please tell Mommy you're okay and you're happy. Will you?"

"Sure I will, Daddy, but why?"

"Well, one day you'll understand that mommies, especially, get sad when their little children grow up."

"Why would she be sad?"

"It's not that Mommy and Daddy don't want you and Meagan to grow up, it's just that time goes by so fast. We get sad when we realize those special times, when you were little, are gone forever. All that remains are the wonderful memories of those times. Remember when Mommy cried on your first day of school? Or when I took down the baby bed because Meagan had outgrown it? Of course we want you and Meagan to grow up and learn new things, but we miss those few short days we had with you as babies and when you were little. But you are growing up. You've grown up a lot since yesterday and it would help Mommy know that you are happy. You have made me happy and it will make her happy, too."

"Sure Dad, I'll tell her."

Avery reached over and held my hand as we walked through the yard, past the swing, and into the back door - at *grandmother's house.*

Stephen Fanning
210-723-8333

<u>steve@stevefanning.com</u>